Learning Mathematics with the Abacus

ACTIVITY BOOK

Year 1

by
Sheikh Faisal Sheikh Mansor
Jamaluddin bin Sabran

KREATIF
KEMBARA

KREATIF KEMBARA SDN. BHD.

ISBN : 983-9278-32-0
© KREATIF KEMBARA SDN. BHD.

KREATIF KEMBARA SDN. BHD.
11, 1st floor, Jalan Mewah, SS22/11,
Damansara Jaya, 47400 Petaling Jaya, Selangor.
Tel : 03-77284400 / 77269431
Fax : 03-77284434
Email : admin@kreatifkembara.com
Printed by : Swan Printing Sdn. Bhd.

Contents

Unit 1　Know your abacus

Can you name the parts of the abacus using the words below?

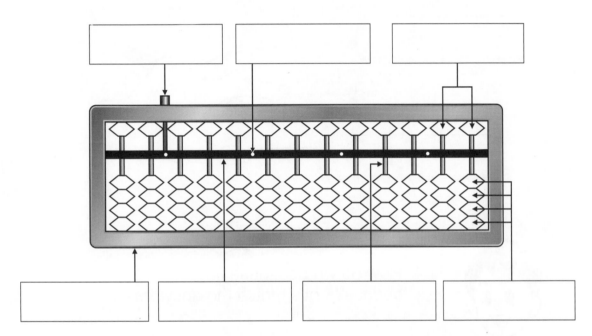

Beam　Frame　Clearing Device　Upper Beads　Dot　Lower Beads　Rod

Can you name these fingers?

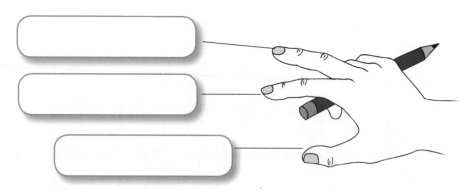

How do we use these fingers on the abacus? Let's match the answers.

thumb

forefinger

middle finger

moves the lower beads towards the beam

moves the upper beads towards and away from the beam

moves the lower beads away from the beam

 This is a butterfly.
Andi is visualising this butterfly.

Can you visualise this butterfly?
Close your eyes and visualise this butterfly.

 How does a ball look like? Can you visualise a ball? Close your eyes and visualise a ball.

Can you visualise the following people?
How do they look like?
Close your eyes and visualise!

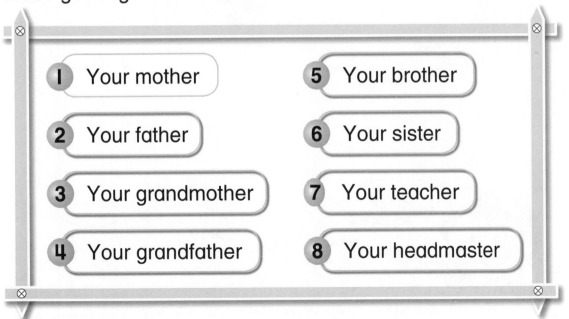

1 Your mother		**5** Your brother	
2 Your father		**6** Your sister	
3 Your grandmother		**7** Your teacher	
4 Your grandfather		**8** Your headmaster	

Activity 1.04

How does your abacus look like?

Close your eyes and visualise your abacus!

Visualise the frame, the beam, the rods, the upper beads and the lower beads.

Can you draw your abacus below?

Unit 2 Numbers 0 to 10

Read and write the following.

one tiger

one

1
one

two swans

two

2
two

three snakes

three

3
three

four flamingos

four

4
four

Can you write the correct numerals and number names below?

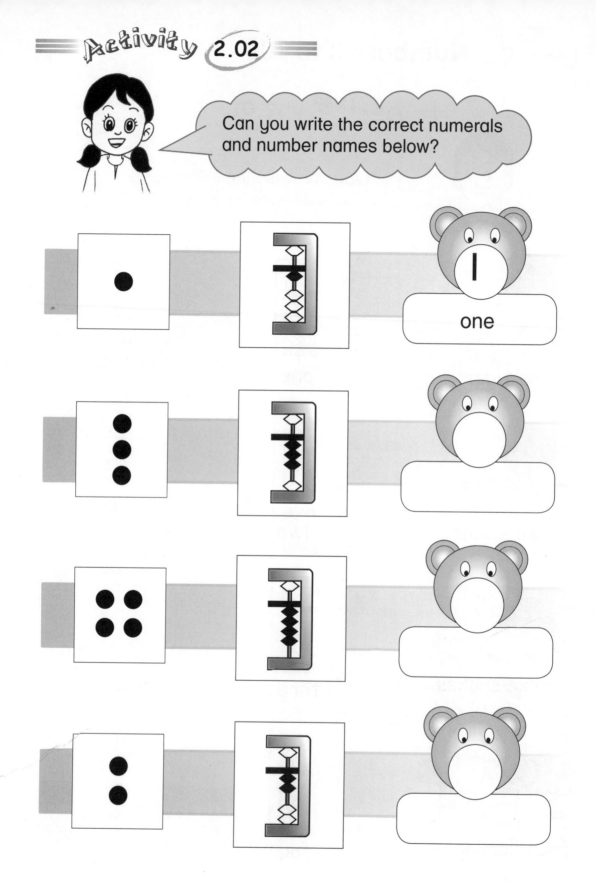

one

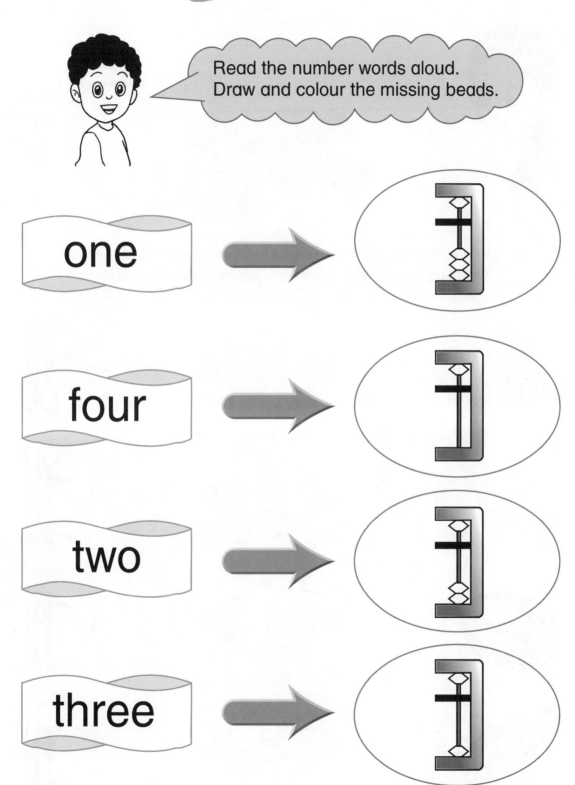

Read the number words aloud.
Draw and colour the missing beads.

one →

four →

two →

three →

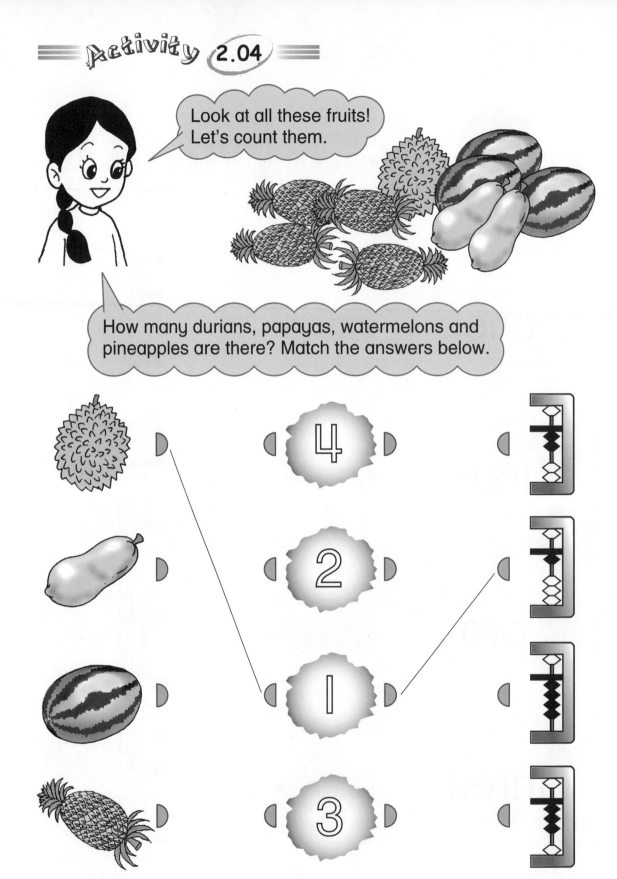

Look at all these fruits! Let's count them.

How many durians, papayas, watermelons and pineapples are there? Match the answers below.

4

2

1

3

Let's move the beads on the abacus!

Move up 1, move down 1

Now, let's try these on your own. Remember to use your thumb and forefinger correctly!

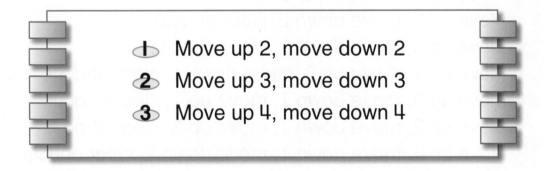

1 Move up 2, move down 2

2 Move up 3, move down 3

3 Move up 4, move down 4

Let's try moving the beads as follows.

Move up 2, move up 1, clear abacus

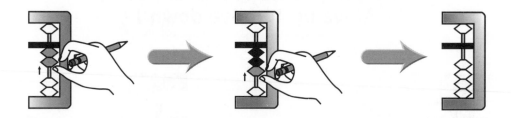

Move up 4, move down 3, move up 2, clear abacus

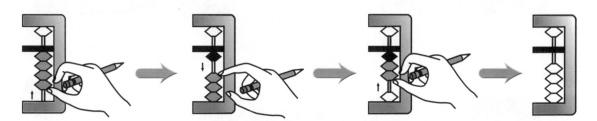

Now, let's try the following on your own.
Use the clearing device to 'clear abacus'.

1	Move up 1, move up 3, clear abacus
2	Move up 4, move down 2, clear abacus
3	Move up 3, move down 1, clear abacus
4	Move up 1, move up 2, move down 1, clear abacus
5	Move up 3, move down 1, move up 1, clear abacus
6	Move up 2, move down 1, move up 3, clear abacus
7	Move up 4, move down 1, move down 2, clear abacus

Close your eyes and visualise the number on the abacus. Then, draw and colour the beads.

one

two

three

four

Read and write the following.

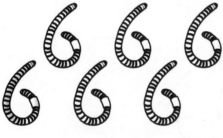

five rabbits

five

six worms

six

seven birds

seven

eight pandas   eight

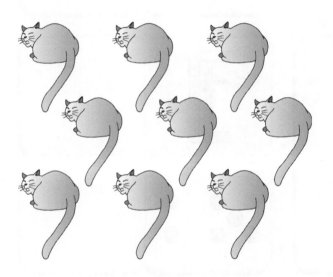

nine cats   nine

Can you count on from 1 to 9?

Write the correct numerals and number names below.

5

five

Read the number words aloud and draw the missing beads.

five

eight

six

nine

seven

Look at all these insects! Let's count each of them.

How many spiders, butterflies, grasshoppers, bees and ants are there?

Activity 2.12

Let's move the beads on the abacus!

Move up 5, move down 5

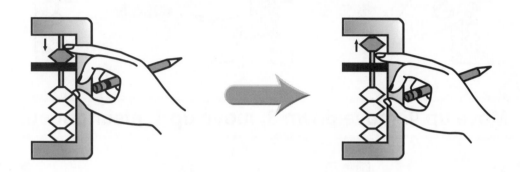

Now, let's try these on your own. Remember to use your thumb, forefinger and middle finger correctly!

1. Move up 6, move down 6
2. Move up 7, move down 7
3. Move up 8, move down 8
4. Move up 9, move down 9

Let's try moving the beads as follows!

Move up 6, move up 3, clear abacus

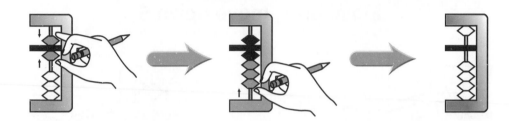

Move up 9, move down 3, move up 1, clear abacus

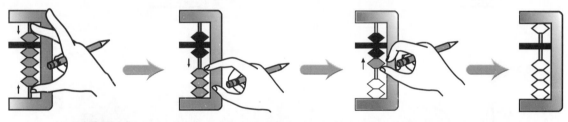

Now, let's try the following on your own.
Use the clearing device to 'clear abacus'.

1 Move up 9, move down 2, clear abacus
2 Move up 8, move down 3, clear abacus
3 Move up 7, move down 1, clear abacus
4 Move up 5, move up 4, clear abacus
5 Move up 5, move up 3, move down 2, clear abacus
6 Move up 7, move down 2, move up 3, clear abacus
7 Move up 6, move down 1, move up 2, clear abacus
8 Move up 8, move down 3, move up 4, clear abacus
9 Move up 9, move down 4, move up 1, clear abacus
10 Move up 5, move up 2, move down 1, clear abacus

Close your eyes and visualise the number on the abacus. Then, draw the beads.

five

six

seven

nine

eight

Let's count on! Write the missing numbers and draw the missing beads.

Let's count back! Write the missing numbers and draw the missing beads.

How does the numeral ten look like?
Write the numeral ten in the box below.

ten

Can you draw the missing beads for the number ten?

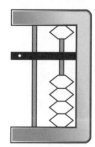

Look at this big house.
It has a door but no windows.
Zero windows!
Can you draw **ten windows** on this house?
Count the windows as you draw them.

Let's match the numbers to the correct beads on the abacus.

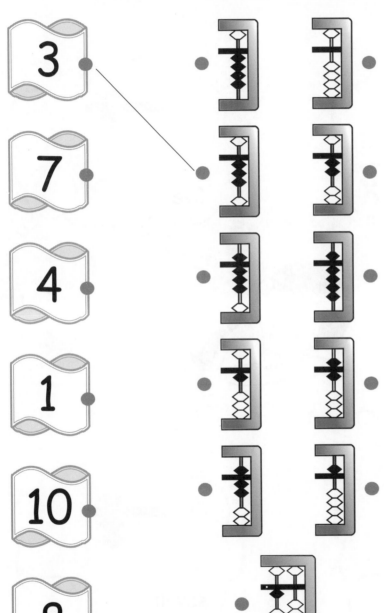
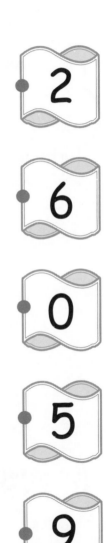

3

7

4

1

10

8

2

6

0

5

9

Let's see if Devi visualises the beads correctly. Mark ✔ if it is correct and ✘ if it is wrong.

three ✘

five

ten

seven

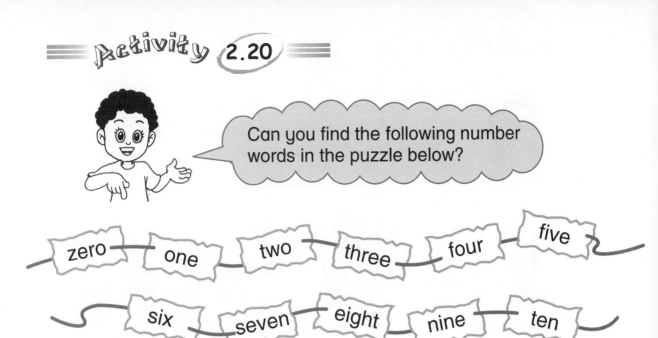

Can you find the following number words in the puzzle below?

zero · one · two · three · four · five · six · seven · eight · nine · ten

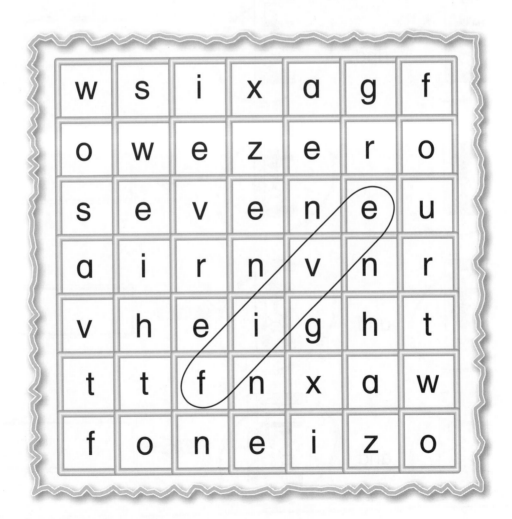

w	s	i	x	a	g	f
o	w	e	z	e	r	o
s	e	v	e	n	e	u
a	i	r	n	v	n	r
v	h	e	i	g	h	t
t	t	f	n	x	a	w
f	o	n	e	i	z	o

Look at the beads and compare them.
Write **equal** or **not equal**.

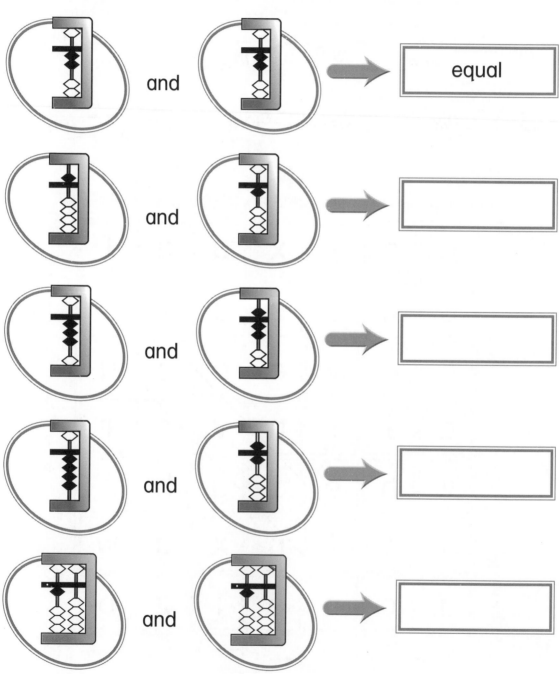

and → equal

and →

and →

and →

and →

Look at the pictures.
Fill in the blanks with **more** or **less**.

Zura has 3 balloons.
Andi has 1 balloon.
3 is _____more_____ than 1.
1 is _____less_____ than 3.

Jenny has 3 fish.
Devi has 5 fish.
3 is _____ than 5.
5 is _____ than 3.

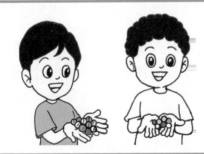

Ah Wai has 10 marbles.
Andi has 7 marbles.
10 is _____ than 7.
7 is _____ than 10.

Devi has 8 flowers.
Zura has 6 flowers.
6 is _____ than 8.
8 is _____ than 6.

Look at the beads and compare them. Write **smaller** or **larger**.

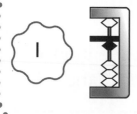 (I) is | smaller | than  (3)

 ( ) is | | than ( )

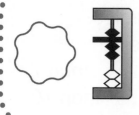 ( ) is | | than   ( )

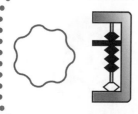 ( ) is | | than 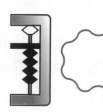 ( )

Let's arrange the following numbers in order **from the smallest to the largest**. Draw the missing beads.

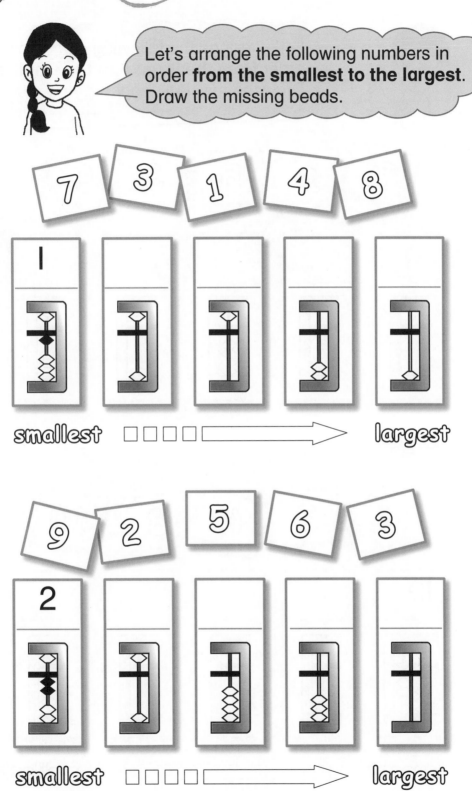

Let's arrange the following numbers in order **from the largest to the smallest**. Draw the missing beads.

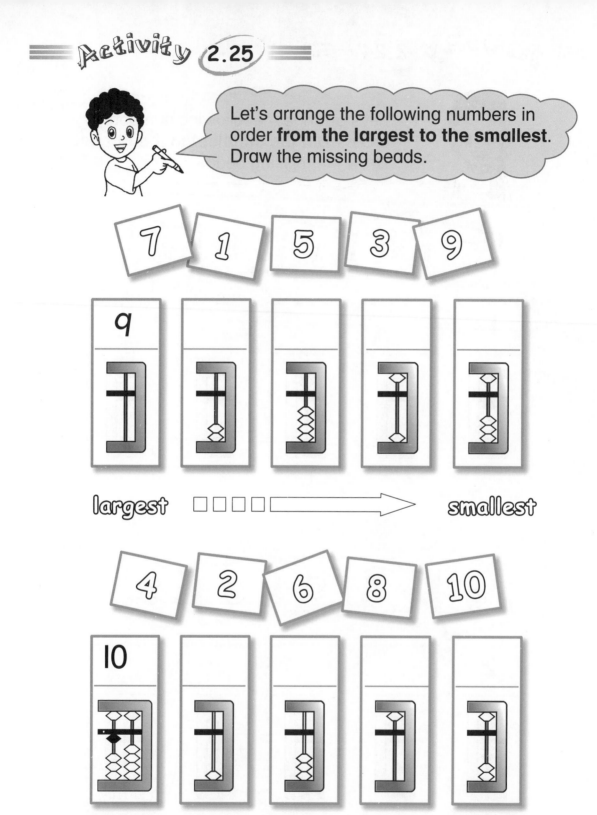

largest ☐☐☐☐ ⟶ smallest

largest ☐☐☐☐ ⟶ smallest

Unit 3   Addition with the highest total of 10

Let's practice with your abacus.
Draw the final bead positions.

- Clear abacus
- Move up 1, move up 1

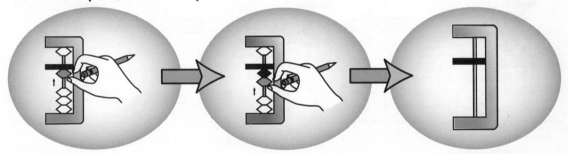

- Clear abacus
- Move up 3, move up 5

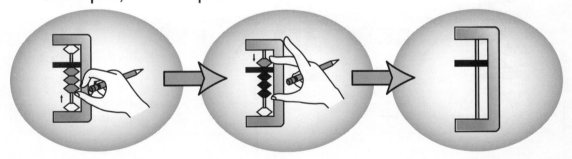

- Clear abacus
- Move up 7, move up 2

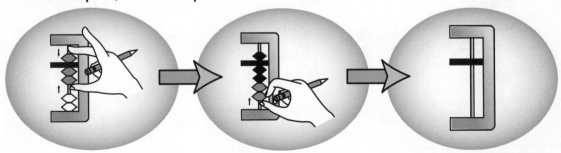

Let's add using the abacus.

What is 3 + 1?

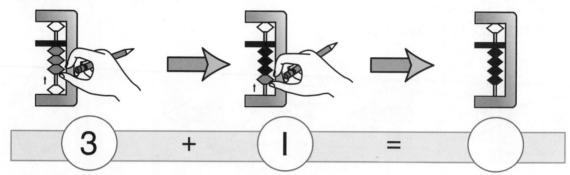

(3) + (1) = ( )

What is 2 + 6?

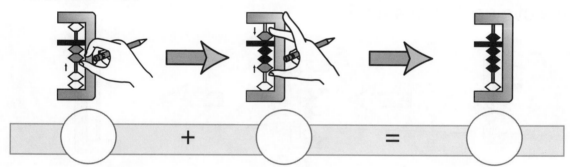

( ) + ( ) = ( )

What is 5 + 4?

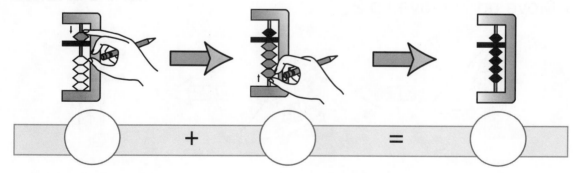

( ) + ( ) = ( )

What is 4 + 5?

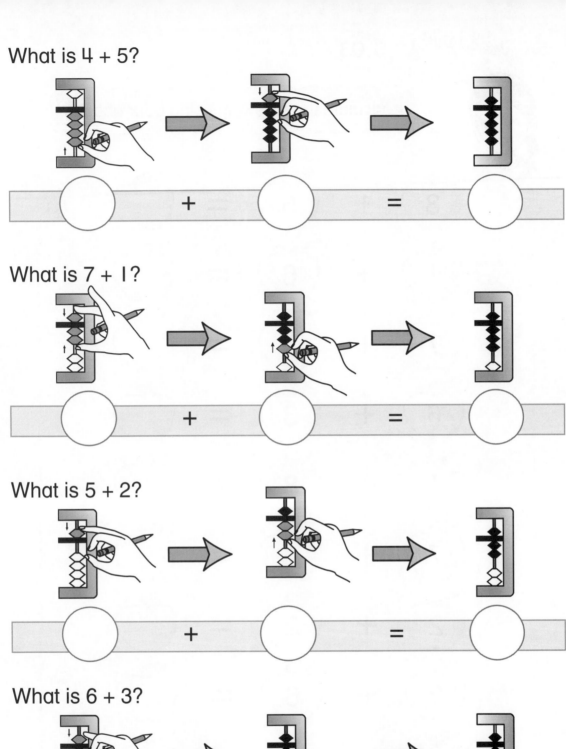

( ) + ( ) = ( )

What is 7 + 1?

( ) + ( ) = ( )

What is 5 + 2?

( ) + ( ) = ( )

What is 6 + 3?

( ) + ( ) = ( )

33

Calculate the following using your abacus.

3 + 5 =

1 + 6 =

7 + 2 =

6 + 3 =

1 + 8 =

7 + 1 =

2 + 2 =

2 + 6 =

5 + 1 =

2 + 1 =

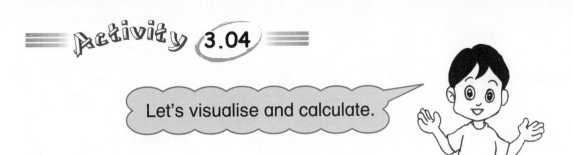
Let's visualise and calculate.

What is 5 + 2?
Visualise and draw the beads.

Step 1: 5, up 5

Step 2: plus 2, up 2

Step 3: equals ☐

| 5 | + | 2 | = | ☐ |

What is 6 + 2?

Step 1: 6, up 6

Step 2: plus 2, up 2

Step 3: equals ☐

6 + 2 = ☐

Can you visualise and calculate these mentally?

1 1 + 1 = ☐

2 2 + 1 = ☐

3 6 + 3 = ☐

4 5 + 3 = ☐

5 8 + 1 = ☐

6 2 + 2 = ☐

Let's visualise 2 apples. Close your eyes and visualise 2 apples.

Now, let's visualise 3 pears.

Can you visualise all these fruits together? Draw 2 apples and 3 pears here.

Can you count the fruits?
How many fruits are there altogether?

Help Andi visualise four cars.
Close your eyes and visualise four cars.
Draw the cars below.

Now, let's visualise and add one more car.
Draw one more car in the space above.

Can you count all the cars?
What is 4 cars plus 1 car?

4 + 1 =

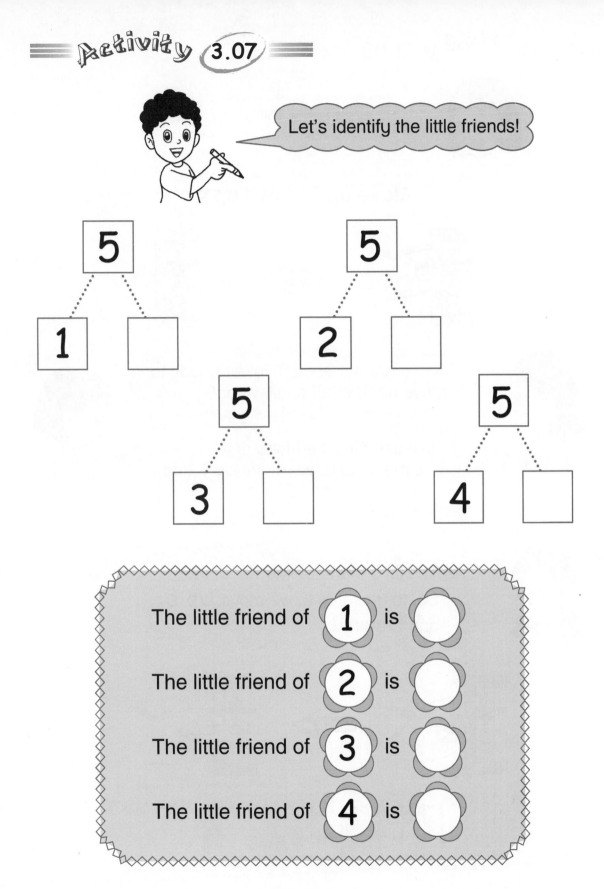

Let's identify the little friends!

5

1 ☐

5

2 ☐

5

3 ☐

5

4 ☐

The little friend of 1 is

The little friend of 2 is

The little friend of 3 is

The little friend of 4 is

Let's try the following.

Move up 1, move up 4

There are not enough lower beads to move up 4. What shall we do?

We use the little friend of 4.
To move up 4, we move **Up 5** and **Down little friend**.

The little friend of 4 is 1.
So, to move up 4, we move **Up 5** and **Down 1**.

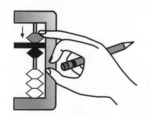 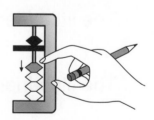

1	+	4	=	

Let's try this!

Move up 3, move up 2

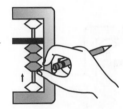 

There are not enough lower beads to move up 2. What shall we do?

We use the little friend of 2. To move up 2, we move **Up 5** and **Down little friend**.

The little friend of 2 is 3. So, to move up 2, we move **Up 5** and **Down 3**.

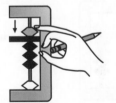 

Let's use the little friend and try these with your abacus.

1	Move up 4, move up 1
2	Move up 2, move up 3

Let's try this with your abacus.
Fill in the blanks.

What is 4 + 3?

Step 1: 4, up ☐

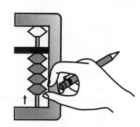

Step 2: plus 3, up 3?

- But there are not enough lower beads to 'up 3'.

- Use the little friend of 3.

- The little friend of 3 is ☐.

- Up 5, Down little friend.

- So, Up 5, Down ☐.

5

3 ☐

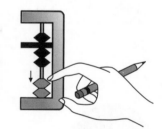

Step 3: equals ☐

4 + 3 = ☐

42

What is 4 + 4?

Step 1: 4, up ☐

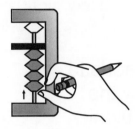

Step 2: plus 4, up 4?

- But there are not enough lower beads to 'up 4'.

- Use the little friend of ☐ .

- The little friend of ☐ is ☐ .

- Up ☐ , Down little friend.

- So, Up ☐ , Down ☐ .

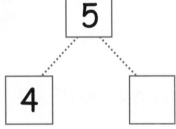

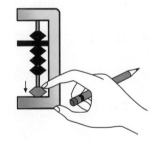

Step 3: equals ☐

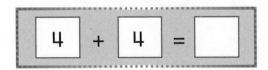

4 + 4 = ☐

Devi has three cats. Jenny has two cats. How many cats are there altogether?

Let's visualise the beads to get the answer. Draw the beads and fill in the blanks.

Step 1: 3, up 3

Step 2: plus 2, up 2?

- But there are not enough lower beads to 'up 2'.

- Use the little friend of 2.

- The little friend of 2 is ☐.

- Up ☐, Down little friend.

- So, Up 5, Down ☐.

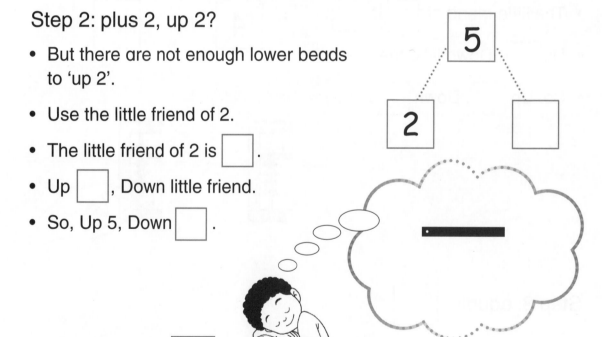

Step 3: equals ☐

There are ☐ cats altogether!

Can you solve these mentally?

0 + 1 = ◯

1 + 0 = ◯

◯ + 1 = 1

◯ + 0 = 1

0 + 2 = ◯

1 + 1 = ◯

2 + 0 = ◯

◯ + 2 = 2

1 + ◯ = 2

◯ + 0 = 2

0 + 3 = ◯

1 + 2 = ◯

2 + 1 = ◯

3 + 0 = ◯

◯ + 3 = 3

1 + ◯ = 3

2 + ◯ = 3

◯ + 0 = 3

0 + 4 = ◯		◯ + 4 = 4
1 + 3 = ◯		1 + ◯ = 4
2 + 2 = ◯		◯ + 2 = 4
3 + 1 = ◯		3 + ◯ = 4
4 + 0 = ◯		◯ + 0 = 4

0 + 5 = ◯		◯ + 5 = 5
1 + 4 = ◯		1 + ◯ = 5
2 + 3 = ◯		◯ + 3 = 5
3 + 2 = ◯		◯ + 2 = 5
4 + 1 = ◯		4 + ◯ = 5
5 + 0 = ◯		◯ + 0 = 5

0 + 6 = ◯		◯ + 6 = 6
1 + 5 = ◯		1 + ◯ = 6
2 + 4 = ◯		◯ + 4 = 6
3 + 3 = ◯		3 + ◯ = 6
4 + 2 = ◯		◯ + 2 = 6
5 + 1 = ◯		5 + ◯ = 6
6 + 0 = ◯		◯ + 0 = 6

0 + 7 = ◯   ◯ + 7 = 7

1 + 6 = ◯   1 + ◯ = 7

2 + 5 = ◯   ◯ + 5 = 7

3 + 4 = ◯   3 + ◯ = 7

4 + 3 = ◯   4 + ◯ = 7

5 + 2 = ◯   ◯ + 2 = 7

6 + 1 = ◯   6 + ◯ = 7

7 + 0 = ◯   ◯ + 0 = 7

0 + 8 = ◯   ◯ + 8 = 8

1 + 7 = ◯   1 + ◯ = 8

2 + 6 = ◯   ◯ + 6 = 8

3 + 5 = ◯   3 + ◯ = 8

4 + 4 = ◯   ◯ + 4 = 8

5 + 3 = ◯   5 + ◯ = 8

6 + 2 = ◯   ◯ + 2 = 8

7 + 1 = ◯   7 + ◯ = 8

8 + 0 = ◯   ◯ + 0 = 8

0 + 9 = ◯   ◯ + 9 = 9

1 + 8 = ◯   1 + ◯ = 9

2 + 7 = ◯   ◯ + 7 = 9

3 + 6 = ◯   3 + ◯ = 9

4 + 5 = ◯   ◯ + 5 = 9

5 + 4 = ◯   ◯ + 4 = 9

6 + 3 = ◯   6 + ◯ = 9

7 + 2 = ◯   ◯ + 2 = 9

8 + 1 = ◯   8 + ◯ = 9

9 + 0 = ◯   ◯ + 0 = 9

Can you find any numbers to fill in the blanks correctly?

◯ + ◯ = 1   ◯ + ◯ = 6

◯ + ◯ = 2   ◯ + ◯ = 7

◯ + ◯ = 3   ◯ + ◯ = 8

◯ + ◯ = 4   ◯ + ◯ = 9

◯ + ◯ = 5   ◯ + ◯ = 0

48

Subtraction within the range of 10

Activity 4.01

Let's visualise 9 balloons.

Now, visualise that 3 of the balloons burst!

Count the number of balloons that are left.

How many balloons are left? ☐

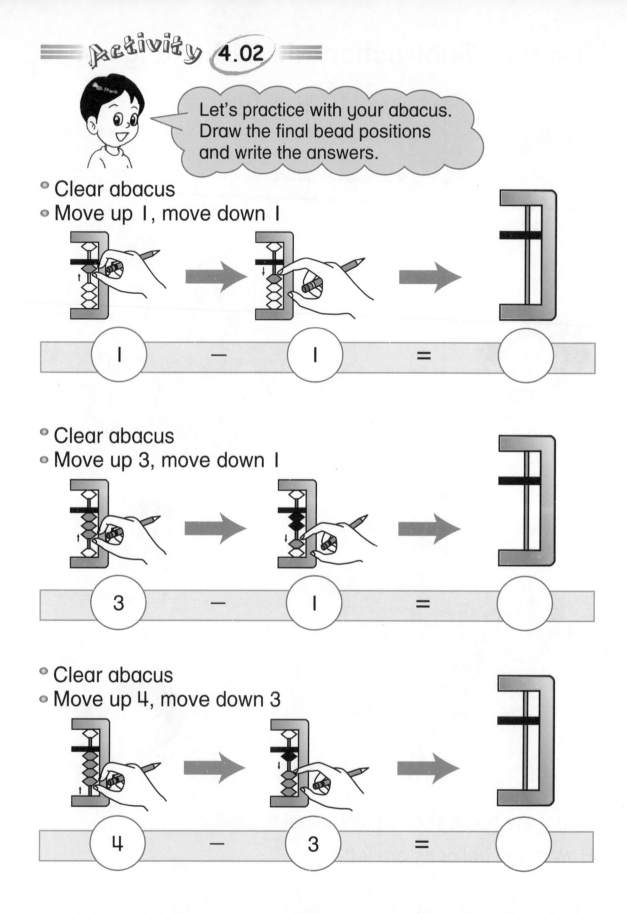

Let's subtract using the abacus!
Fill in the blanks with the answers.

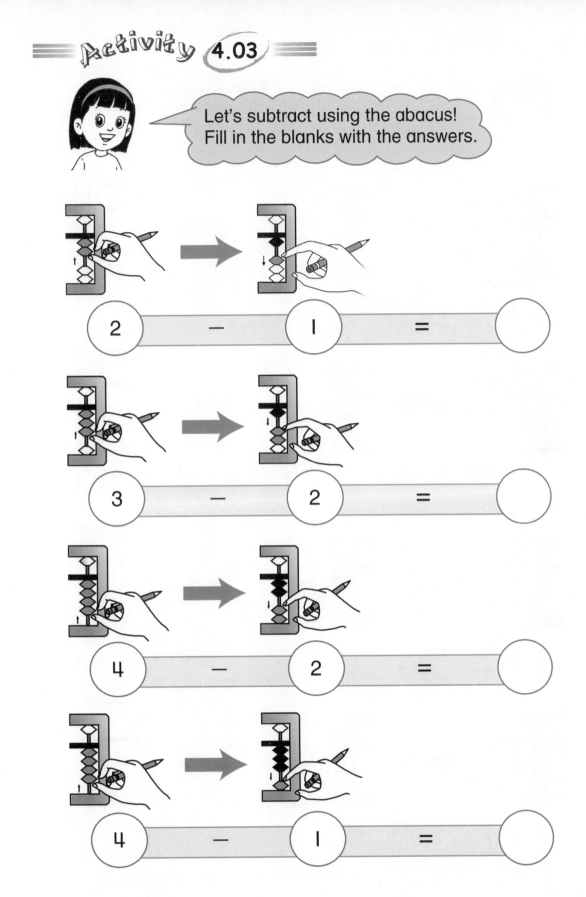

2 — 1 =

3 — 2 =

4 — 2 =

4 — 1 =

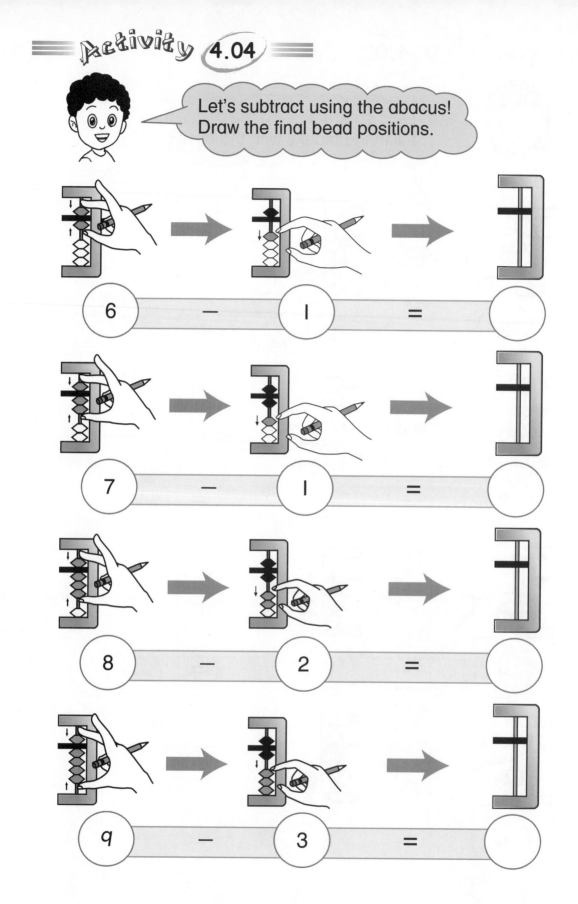

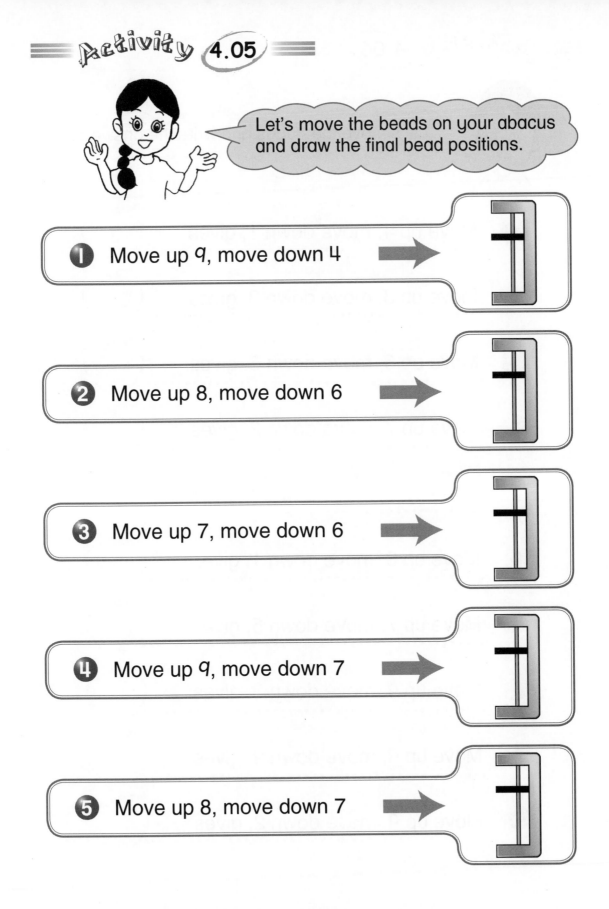

Let's move the beads and write the answers.

1 Move up 4, move down 1, gives 3

2 Move up 3, move down 3, gives ....

3 Move up 6, move down 5, gives ....

4 Move up 7, move down 2, gives ....

5 Move up 8, move down 3, gives ....

6 Move up 8, move down 1, gives ....

7 Move up 7, move down 5, gives ....

8 Move up 9, move down 3, gives ....

9 Move up 9, move down 9, gives ....

10 Move up 9, move down 2, gives ....

Calculate the following using your abacus.

2 − 2 =

6 − 1 =

8 − 5 =

7 − 7 =

q − 8 =

q − 1 =

q − 5 =

8 − 1 =

7 − 6 =

8 − 6 =

Let's visualise and calculate.

What is 4 − 2?
Visualise and draw the beads.

Step 1: 4, up 4

Step 2: minus 2, down 2

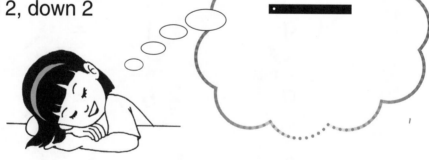

Step 3: equals ☐

4 − 2 = ☐

What is 9 − 6?

Step 1: 9, up 9

Step 2: minus 6, down 6

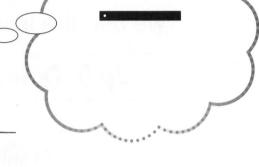

Step 3: equals [ ]

$$9 - 6 = \boxed{}$$

Can you visualise and calculate these mentally?

1 8 − 3 = [ ]

2 3 − 2 = [ ]

3 7 − 5 = [ ]

4 7 − 6 = [ ]

5 9 − 4 = [ ]

6 9 − 7 = [ ]

How do we use the little friend in subtraction?

In addition,

we use the little friend like this:

Up 5, Down little friend

In subtraction,

we use the little friend like this:

| | little friend, | | 5 |

Do you still remember the little friends?
Write them down in the boxes below.

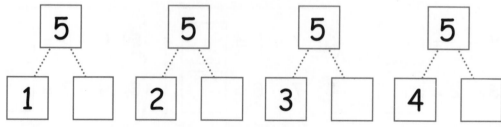

5   5   5   5

1 ☐   2 ☐   3 ☐   4 ☐

Let's try the following.

Move up 5, move down 1

There are not enough lower beads to move down 1. What shall we do?

We use the little friend of 1. To move down 1, we move **Up little friend** and **Down 5**.

The little friend of 1 is 4. So, to move down 1, we move **Up 4** and **Down 5**.

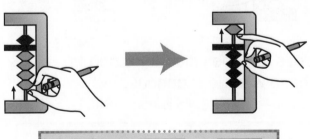

5	–	1	=	

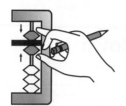 Let's try this!

Move up 6, move down 3

 There are not enough lower beads to move down 3. What shall we do?

We use the little friend of 3. To move down 3, we move **Up little friend** and **Down 5**.

 The little friend of 3 is 2. So, to move down 3, we move **Up 2** and **Down 5**.

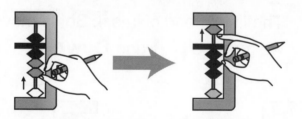

 Let's use the little friend and try these with your abacus.

I	Move up 6, move down 4
2	Move up 6, move down 2

Let's try this with your abacus.
Fill in the blanks.

What is 8 – 4?

Step 1: 8, up ☐

Step 2: minus 4, down 4?

- But there are not enough lower beads to 'down 4'.

- Use the little friend of 4.

- The little friend of 4 is ☐ .

- Up little friend, Down 5.

- So, Up ☐ , Down 5.

5

4   ☐

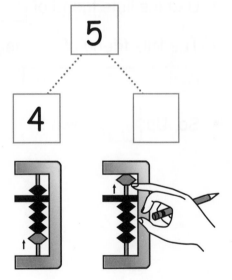

Step 3: equals ☐

8 – 4 = ☐

What is 5 − 3?

Step 1: 5, up ☐

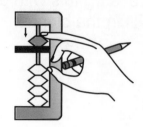

Step 2: minus 3, down 3?

- But there are not enough lower beads to 'down 3'.

- Use the little friend of ☐.

- The little friend of ☐ is ☐.

- Up ☐☐☐☐☐☐, Down 5.

- So, Up ☐, Down 5.

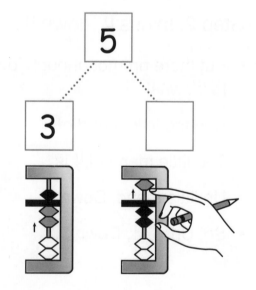

Step 3: equals ☐

5 − 3 = ☐

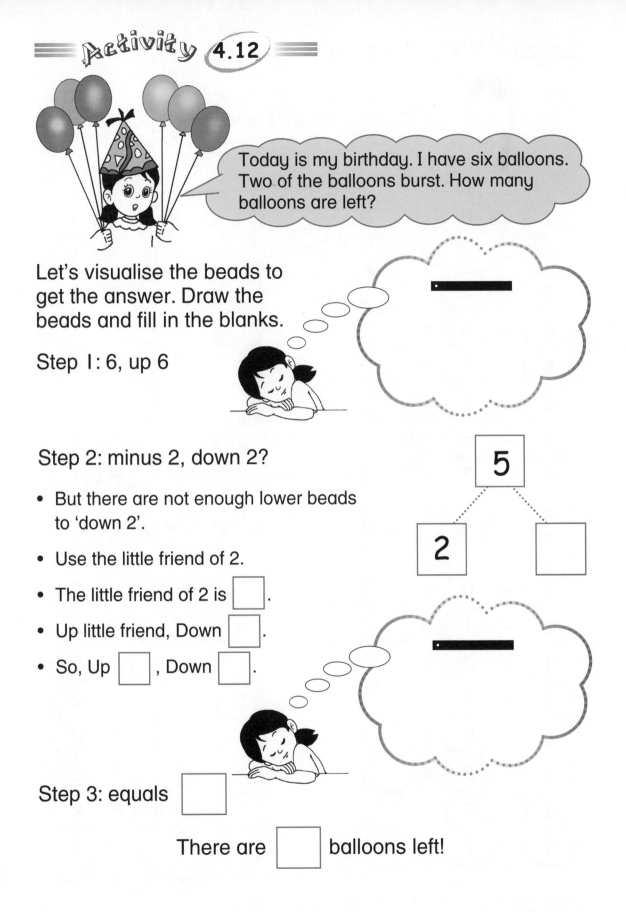

Today is my birthday. I have six balloons. Two of the balloons burst. How many balloons are left?

Let's visualise the beads to get the answer. Draw the beads and fill in the blanks.

Step 1: 6, up 6

Step 2: minus 2, down 2?

- But there are not enough lower beads to 'down 2'.
- Use the little friend of 2.
- The little friend of 2 is ☐.
- Up little friend, Down ☐.
- So, Up ☐ , Down ☐.

5

2 ☐

Step 3: equals ☐

There are ☐ balloons left!

Can you solve these mentally?

1 − 0 = ◯   1 − ◯ = 1
2 − 1 = ◯   ◯ − 1 = 1
3 − 2 = ◯   3 − ◯ = 1
4 − 3 = ◯   ◯ − 3 = 1
5 − 4 = ◯   5 − ◯ = 1
6 − 5 = ◯   ◯ − 5 = 1
7 − 6 = ◯   7 − ◯ = 1
8 − 7 = ◯   ◯ − 7 = 1
q − 8 = ◯   q − ◯ = 1

2 − 0 = ◯   ◯ − 0 = 2
3 − 1 = ◯   3 − ◯ = 2
4 − 2 = ◯   ◯ − 2 = 2
5 − 3 = ◯   5 − ◯ = 2
6 − 4 = ◯   ◯ − 4 = 2
7 − 5 = ◯   7 − ◯ = 2
8 − 6 = ◯   ◯ − 6 = 2
q − 7 = ◯   q − ◯ = 2

$3 - 0 = \bigcirc$ $3 - \bigcirc = 3$

$4 - 1 = \bigcirc$ $\bigcirc - 1 = 3$

$5 - 2 = \bigcirc$ $5 - \bigcirc = 3$

$6 - 3 = \bigcirc$ $\bigcirc - 3 = 3$

$7 - 4 = \bigcirc$ $7 - \bigcirc = 3$

$8 - 5 = \bigcirc$ $\bigcirc - 5 = 3$

$9 - 6 = \bigcirc$ $9 - \bigcirc = 3$

$4 - 0 = \bigcirc$ $\bigcirc - 0 = 4$

$5 - 1 = \bigcirc$ $5 - \bigcirc = 4$

$6 - 2 = \bigcirc$ $\bigcirc - 2 = 4$

$7 - 3 = \bigcirc$ $7 - \bigcirc = 4$

$8 - 4 = \bigcirc$ $\bigcirc - 4 = 4$

$9 - 5 = \bigcirc$ $9 - \bigcirc = 4$

$5 - 0 = \bigcirc$ $5 - \bigcirc = 5$

$6 - 1 = \bigcirc$ $\bigcirc - 1 = 5$

$7 - 2 = \bigcirc$ $7 - \bigcirc = 5$

$8 - 3 = \bigcirc$ $\bigcirc - 3 = 5$

$9 - 4 = \bigcirc$ $9 - \bigcirc = 5$

6 − 0 = ◯   ◯ − 0 = 6
7 − 1 = ◯   7 − ◯ = 6
8 − 2 = ◯   ◯ − 2 = 6
9 − 3 = ◯   9 − ◯ = 6

7 − 0 = ◯   7 − ◯ = 7
8 − 1 = ◯   ◯ − 1 = 7
9 − 2 = ◯   9 − ◯ = 7

8 − 0 = ◯   ◯ − 0 = 8
9 − 1 = ◯   9 − ◯ = 8

9 − 0 = ◯   ◯ − 0 = 9

Can you find any numbers to fill in the blanks correctly?
Fill them in.

◯ − ◯ = 1   ◯ − ◯ = 6
◯ − ◯ = 2   ◯ − ◯ = 7
◯ − ◯ = 3   ◯ − ◯ = 8
◯ − ◯ = 4   ◯ − ◯ = 9
◯ − ◯ = 5   ◯ − ◯ = 10

 Unit 5 **Numbers up to 20**

Say the number words aloud.
Match them to the correct numerals.

twelve

eighteen

eleven

fifteen

twenty

thirteen

seventeen

fourteen

nineteen

sixteen

ten

13

15

12

20

16

11

17

14

18

10

19

Activity 5.02

How many carrots are there in the baskets?
Count them and match the answers.

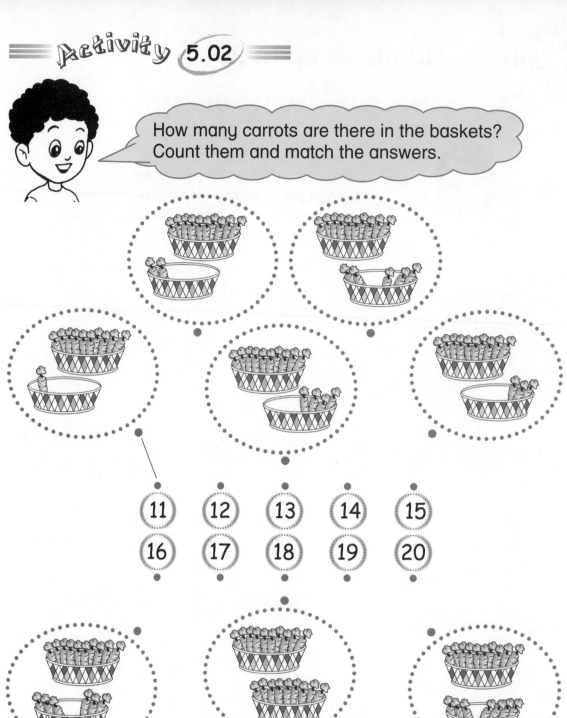

68

Write the numbers correctly.

1 1 ten and 4 ones ➡ 14

2 1 ten and 0 one ➡

3 1 ten and 7 ones ➡

4 1 ten and 5 ones ➡

5 1 ten and 3 ones ➡

6 1 ten and 8 ones ➡

7 2 tens and 0 one ➡

8 1 ten and 1 one ➡

9 1 ten and 9 ones ➡

10 1 ten and 2 ones ➡

11 1 ten and 6 ones ➡

Draw the missing beads representing each number.

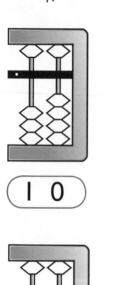

1 0

1 1

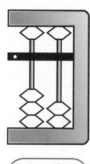

1 2

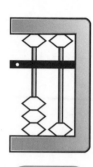

1 3

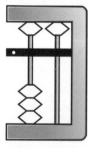

1 4

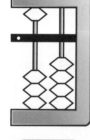

1 5

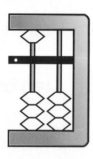

1 6

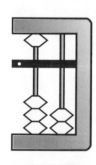

1 7

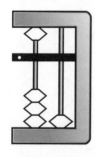

1 8

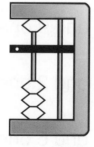

1 9

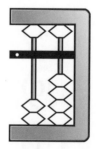

2 0

70

Write the correct number words.

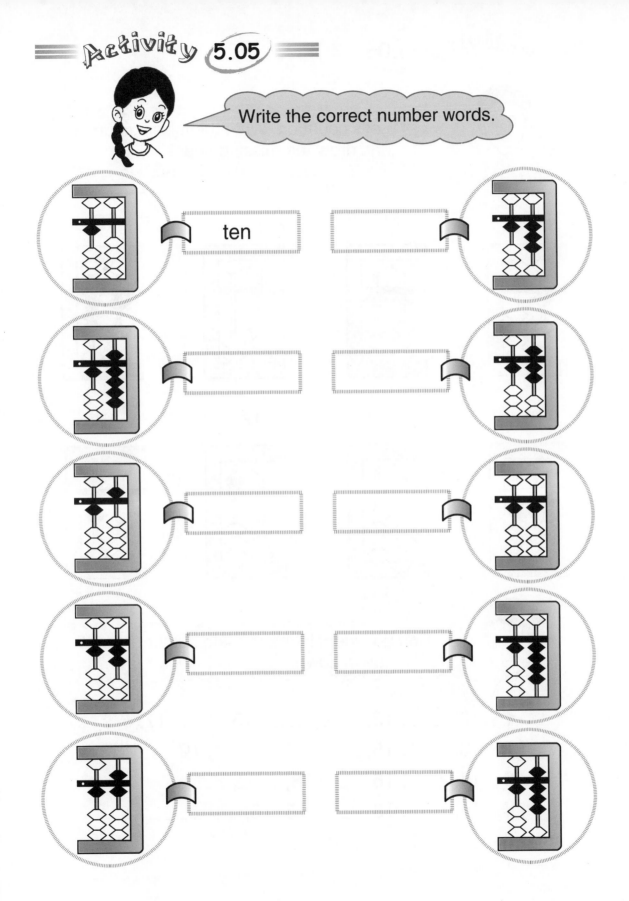

ten

Let's count on! Write the missing numbers and draw the missing beads.

10,   11,   ☐,   13

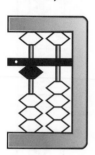 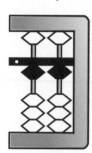 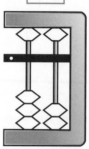 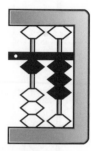

14,   ☐,   16,   17

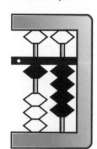 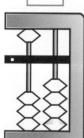  

Can you identify the missing numbers here? Write them down.

1 10, ____, 12, ____, ____, 15, ____, 17.

2 13, ____, 15, ____, ____, ____, 19, ____.

3 14, ____, 16, ____, 18, ____, ____.

4 11, ____, 13, ____, 15, 16, ____, ____.

5 ____, 17, ____, 19, ____.

Let's count back! Write the missing numbers and draw the missing beads.

20, □, 18, 17

 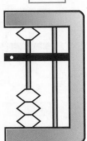 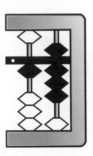 

15, 14, □, 12

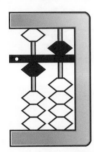 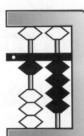 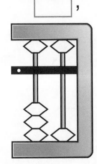 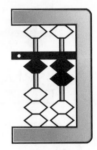

Can you identify the missing numbers here?

1 20, ____, 18, ____, 16, ____, 14.

2 17, ____, 15, ____, ____, ____, 11, 10.

3 14, ____, ____, 11, ____.

4 19, ____, ____, 16, ____, 14, ____.

5 ____, 17, ____, 15, ____, 13, ____.

Let' move the beads on the abacus.

Move up 12, move down 12

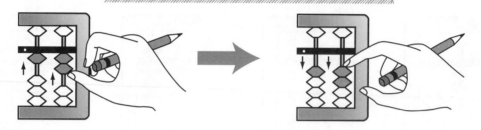

Move up 13, move down 13

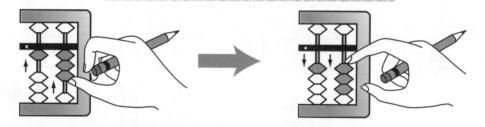

Now, let's try these on your own.
Remember to use your fingers correctly!

1. Move up 10, move down 10
2. Move up 11, move down 11
3. Move up 14, move down 14
4. Move up 15, move down 15
5. Move up 16, move down 16
6. Move up 17, move down 17
7. Move up 18, move down 18
8. Move up 19, move down 19
9. Move up 20, move down 20

Activity 5.09

Let's visualise and draw the beads.

Jenny has 13 flowers.

Andi has 20 marbles.

Ah Wai has 15 eggs.

Zura has 17 rambutans.

Unit 6 Addition with the highest total of 18

Let' practise with your abacus.

Move up 10, move up 1, clear abacus

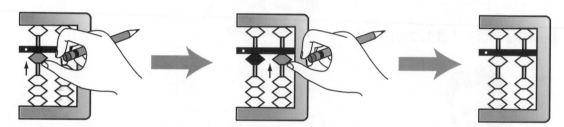

Now, let's try these on your own.
Use the clearing device to 'clear abacus'.

1 Move up 16, move up 3, clear abacus
2 Move up 13, move up 6, clear abacus
3 Move up 11, move up 8, clear abacus
4 Move up 10, move up 9, clear abacus
5 Move up 15, move up 4, clear abacus
6 Move up 12, move up 2, clear abacus
7 Move up 2, move up 11, clear abacus
8 Move up 6, move up 12, clear abacus
9 Move up 8, move up 10, clear abacus
10 Move up 3, move up 15, clear abacus
11 Move up 1, move up 17, clear abacus
12 Move up 3, move up 11, clear abacus

Move the beads and draw the final bead positions.

1 Move up 10, move up 8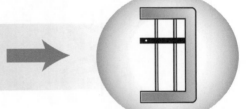

2 Move up 16, move up 2

3 Move up 10, move up 7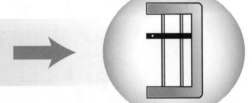

4 Move up 13, move up 5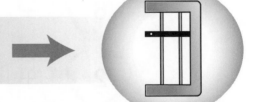

5 Move up 11, move up 6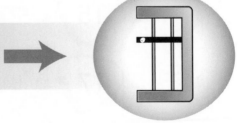

Let's use the abacus to calculate!

10 + 7 = ♡

11 + 6 = ♡

7 + 11 = ♡

11 + 3 = ♡

13 + 5 = ♡

6 + 12 = ♡

6 + 10 = ♡

2 + 12 = ♡

15 + 2 = ♡

17 + 1 = ♡

Activity 6.04

1 Move up 3, move up 10

2 Move up 12, move up 6

3 Move up 2, move up 15

 Can you visualise and calculate these mentally?

1 10 + 3 = ♡   **4** 5 + 12 = ♡

2 12 + 5 = ♡   **5** 7 + 11 = ♡

3 17 + 1 = ♡   **6** 2 + 16 = ♡

Let's count and fill in the blanks!

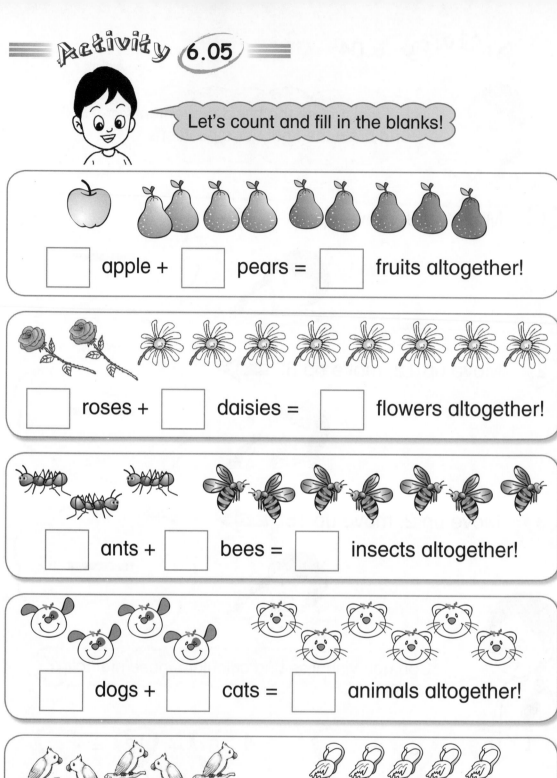

[ ] apple + [ ] pears = [ ] fruits altogether!

[ ] roses + [ ] daisies = [ ] flowers altogether!

[ ] ants + [ ] bees = [ ] insects altogether!

[ ] dogs + [ ] cats = [ ] animals altogether!

[ ] parrots + [ ] flamingos = [ ] birds altogether!

Let's identify the big friends! Can you guess the missing numbers?

1 + ⬭ = 10

2 + 8 = ⬭

3 + 7 = ⬭

4 + ⬭ = 10

5 + 5 = ⬭

6 + ⬭ = 10

7 + ⬭ = 10

8 + ⬭ = 10

9 + 1 = ⬭

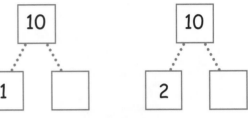

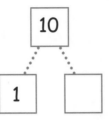

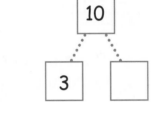

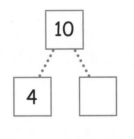

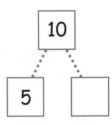

The big friend of 1 is ⬭

The big friend of 2 is ⬭

The big friend of 3 is ⬭

The big friend of 4 is ⬭

The big friend of 5 is ⬭

The big friend of 9 is ⬭

The big friend of 8 is ⬭

The big friend of 7 is ⬭

The big friend of 6 is ⬭

How do we use the big friend to add numbers?

Let's try $1 + 9$. Use your abacus and follow us!

Move up 1, move up 9

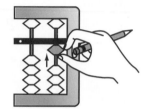 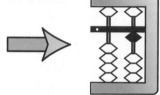

There are not enough beads at Ones to move up 9. What shall we do?

We use the big friend of 9. To move up 9, we move
Down big friend at Ones and **Carry 1 at Tens**.

The big friend of 9 is 1. So, to move up 9, we move
Down 1 at Ones and Carry 1 at Tens.

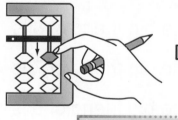 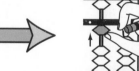 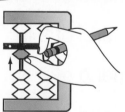 

1	+	9	=	

Let's try 7 + 4.

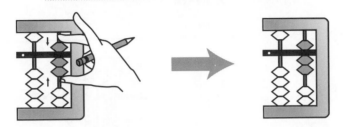

Move up 7, move up 4

There are not enough beads at Ones to move up 4. What shall we do?

We use the big friend of 4. To move up 4, we move **Down big friend at Ones** and **Carry 1 at Tens**.

The big friend of 4 is 6. So, to move up 4, we move **Down 6 at Ones** and **Carry 1 at Tens**.

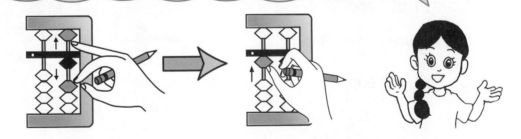

Let's use the big friend and try these with your abacus.

1	Move up 5, move up 5
2	Move up 9, move up 8
3	Move up 8, move up 7

Let's try this with your abacus.
Fill in the blanks.

What is 8 + 8?

Step 1: 8, up ☐

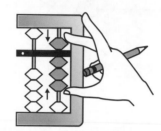

Step 2: plus 8, up 8?

- But there are not enough beads at Ones to 'up 8'.

- Use the big friend of 8.

- The big friend of 8 is ☐ .

- Down big friend at Ones, Carry 1 at Tens.

- So, Down ☐ at Ones,

  Carry 1 at Tens.

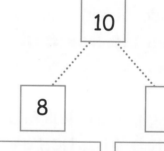

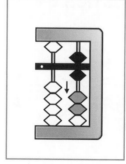

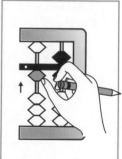

Step 3: equals ☐

| 8 | + | 8 | = | ☐ |

What is $9 + 7$?

Step 1: 9, up ☐

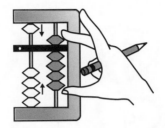

Step 2: plus 7, up 7?

- But there are not enough beads at Ones to 'up 7'.

- Use the big friend of 7.

- The big friend of 7 is ☐.

- Down big friend at Ones, Carry 1 at Tens.

- So, Down ☐ at Ones,

  Carry 1 at Tens.

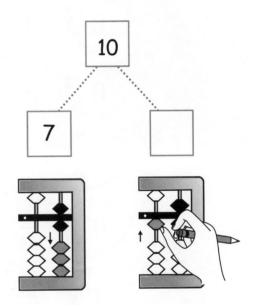

Step 3: equals ☐

Use the big friend to solve these with your abacus.

7 + 3 =

9 + 1 =

6 + 4 =

8 + 5 =

9 + 2 =

9 + 7 =

4 + 8 =

9 + 6 =

9 + 9 =

6 + 5 =

Sometimes the big friend needs help from the little friend! Let's try this with your abacus.

What is 5 + 6?

Step 1: 5, up ☐

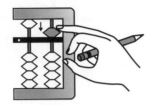

Step 2: plus 6, up 6?

- But there are not enough beads at Ones to 'up 6'.
- Use the big friend of 6.
- The big friend of 6 is 4.
- Down big friend at Ones, Carry 1 at Tens.
- So, Down 4 at Ones, Carry 1 at Tens.
- But there are not enough beads at Ones to 'down 4'.
- Use little friend to help big friend.
- The little friend of 4 is ☐ .
- Down 4 is Up little friend, Down 5.
- So, Up ☐ , Down 5, Carry 1 at Tens.

10   5

6   4   ☐

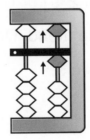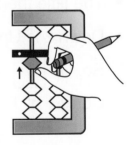

Step 3: equals ☐

5 + 6 = ☐

87

Let's try this with your abacus.

What is 5 + 8?

Step 1: 5, up ☐

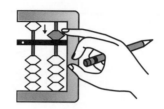

Step 2: plus 8, up 8?

- But there are not enough beads at Ones to 'up 8'.
- Use the big friend of 8.
- The big friend of 8 is 2.
- Down big friend at Ones, Carry 1 at Tens.
- So, Down 2 at Ones, Carry 1 at Tens.
- But there are not enough beads at Ones to 'down 2'.
- Use little friend to help big friend.
- The little friend of 2 is ☐.
- Down 2 is Up little friend, Down 5.
- So, Up ☐, Down 5, Carry 1 at Tens.

10		5
8	2	☐

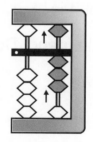 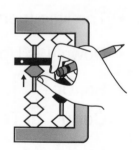

Step 3: equals ☐

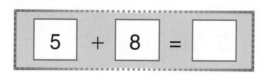

5 + 8 = ☐

Activity 6.11

Try this!

What is 7 + 7?

Step 1: 7, up ☐

Step 2: plus 7, up 7?

- But there are not enough beads at Ones to 'up 7'.

- Use the big friend of 7.

- The big friend of 7 is ☐.

- Down big friend at Ones, Carry 1 at Tens.

- So, Down ☐ at Ones, Carry 1 at Tens.

- But there are not enough beads at Ones to Down ☐.

- Use little friend to help big friend.

- The little friend of ☐ is ☐.

- Down ☐ is Up little friend, Down 5.

- So, Up ☐, Down 5, Carry 1 at Tens.

```
        10          5
   7         ☐          ☐
```

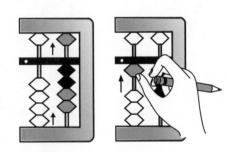

Step 3: equals ☐

$$7 \; + \; 7 \; = \; \boxed{}$$

Can you write the missing numbers?

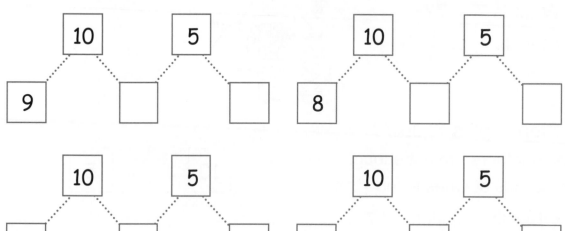

| 10 | 5 | | 10 | 5 |
| 9 | □ | □ | 8 | □ | □ |

| 10 | 5 | | 10 | 5 |
| 7 | □ | □ | 6 | □ | □ |

Try solving these with your abacus.

6	+	8	=	□
6	+	7	=	□
5	+	9	=	□
6	+	6	=	□
7	+	6	=	□

Unit 7 Subtraction within the range of 18

Let's practise with your abacus.

Move up 18, move down 6, clear abacus

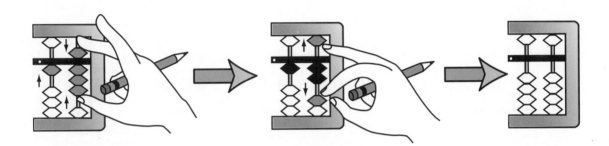

Now, let's try the following on your own.
Use the clearing device to 'clear abacus'.

1 Move up 11, move down 1, clear abacus
2 Move up 13, move down 2, clear abacus
3 Move up 18, move down 5, clear abacus
4 Move up 17, move down 7, clear abacus
5 Move up 13, move down 2, clear abacus
6 Move up 14, move down 3, clear abacus
7 Move up 12, move down 10, clear abacus
8 Move up 14, move down 11, clear abacus
9 Move up 17, move down 16, clear abacus
10 Move up 17, move down 12, clear abacus

Move the beads and draw the final bead positions.

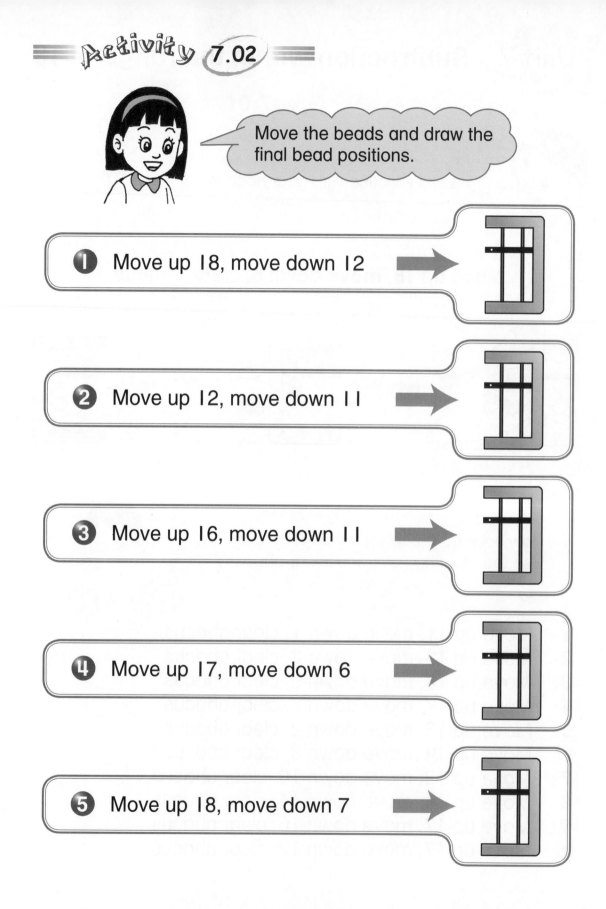

1 Move up 18, move down 12

2 Move up 12, move down 11

3 Move up 16, move down 11

4 Move up 17, move down 6

5 Move up 18, move down 7

Let's use the abacus to calculate!

15 − 15 =

14 − 13 =

17 − 11 =

18 − 8 =

18 − 11 =

17 − 16 =

14 − 12 =

15 − 5 =

12 − 1 =

18 − 13 =

1 Move up 13, move down 3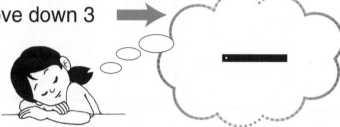

2 Move up 16, move down 5

3 Move up 17, move down 12

Can you visualise and calculate these mentally?

1 18 − 5 = ♡   **4** 18 − 3 = ♡

2 17 − 15 = ♡   **5** 13 − 1 = ♡

3 18 − 10 = ♡   **6** 16 − 16 = ♡

Sometimes we need to use the big friend to subtract. How do we use the big friend in subtraction?

In addition,

we use the big friend like this:

> **Down big friend at Ones,**
> **Carry 1 at Tens**

In subtraction,

we use the big friend like this:

> 1 at Tens,
> big friend at Ones.

Let's try 15 − 9.
Use your abacus and follow us!

Move up 15, move down 9

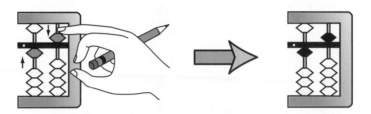

There are not enough beads at Ones
to move down 9. What shall we do?

We use the big friend of 9. To move down 9,
Remove 1 at Tens and **Up big friend at Ones**.

The big friend of 9 is 1. So, to move down 9,
Remove 1 at Tens and **Up 1 at Ones**.

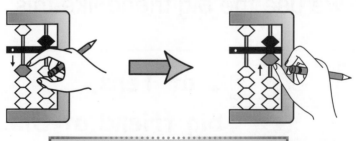

15	−	9	=	

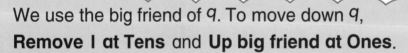

Let's try this with your abacus.
Fill in the blanks.

What is 12 − 8?

Step 1: 12, up ☐

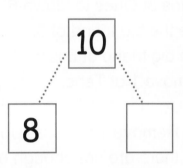

Step 2: minus 8, down 8?

- But there are not enough beads at Ones to 'down 8'.

- Use the big friend of 8.

- The big friend of 8 is ☐.

- Remove 1 at Tens,
  Up big friend at Ones.

- So, Remove 1 at Tens,

    Up ☐ at Ones.

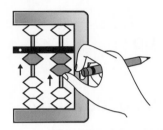

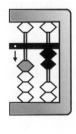

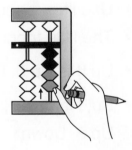

Step 3: equals ☐

12 − 8 = ☐

97

Again, sometimes the big friend needs help from the little friend! Let's try this with your abacus.

What is 11 − 6?

Step 1: 11, up ☐

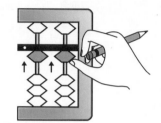

Step 2: minus 6, down 6?
- But there are not enough beads at Ones to 'down 6'.
- Use the big friend of 6.
- The big friend of 6 is 4.
- Remove 1 at Tens, Up big friend at Ones.
- So, Remove 1 at Tens, Up 4 at Ones.
- But there are not enough beads at Ones to 'up 4'.
- Use little friend to help big friend.
- The little friend of 4 is ☐ .
- Up 4 is Up 5, Down little friend.
- So, Remove 1 at Tens, Up 5, Down ☐ .

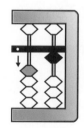 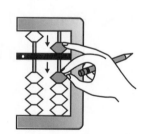

Step 3: equals ☐

11 − 6 = ☐

98

Activity 7.09

Let's try this!

What is 13 − 7?

Step 1: 13, up ☐

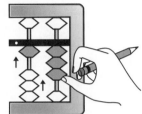

Step 2: minus 7, down 7?

- But there are not enough beads at Ones to 'down 7'.

- Use the big friend of 7.

- The big friend of 7 is ☐ .

- Remove 1 at Tens, Up big friend at Ones.

- So, Remove 1 at Tens, Up ☐ at Ones.

- But there are not enough beads at Ones to 'up ☐ '.

- Use little friend to help big friend.

- The little friend of ☐ is ☐ .

- Up ☐ is Up 5, Down little friend.

- So, Remove 1 at Tens, Up 5, Down ☐ .

```
   10          5
  /   \       /   \
 7      ☐    ☐
```

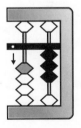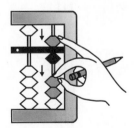

Step 3: equals ☐

| 13 | − | 7 | = | ☐ |

99

Calculate the following using your abacus.

1. 10 − 1 =

2. 14 − 5 =

3. 11 − 9 =

4. 12 − 5 =

5. 13 − 6 =

6. 11 − 3 =

7. 11 − 6 =

8. 14 − 9 =

9. 14 − 7 =

10. 11 − 8 =

11. 10 − 5 =

12. 17 − 8 =

13. 15 − 7 =

14. 16 − 7 =

15. 14 − 8 =

16. 12 − 7 =

17. 13 − 9 =

18. 10 − 3 =

19. 12 − 6 =

20. 13 − 4 =

You may need to get the little friend to help the big friend!

Unit 8 Numbers up to 100

Activity 8.01

 Read the number words aloud. Write the numerals and draw the missing beads.

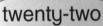 twenty-two — 22
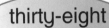 thirty-eight
forty

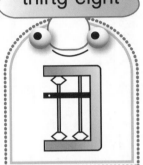
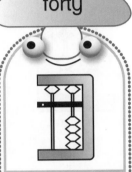

forty-seven
fifty-three
sixty-one

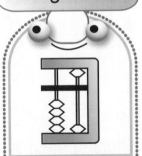

seventy-nine
eighty-five
ninety-four

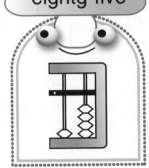

Let's count on! Write the missing numbers and draw the missing beads.

41,   42,   ☐,   44

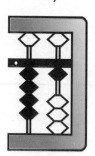  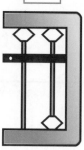 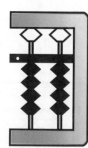

76,   ☐,   78,   79

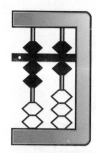 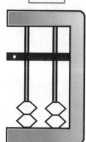 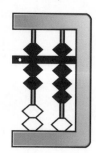 

Can you identify the missing numbers here? Write them down.

1 21, ____, 23, ____, ____, 26, ____, 28.

2 64, ____, 66, ____, ____, ____, 70, ____.

3 88, ____, 90, ____, 92, ____, ____ 95.

4 52, ____, 54, ____, 56, 57, ____, ____.

5 ____, 33, ____, 35, ____, ____, 38, ____.

Let's count back! Write the missing numbers and draw the missing beads.

34,   ☐,   32,   31

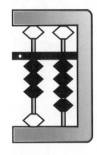  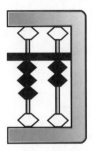 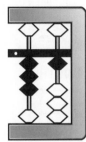

71,   70,   ☐,   68

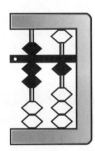 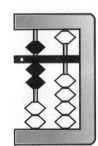 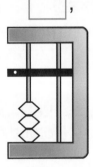 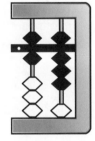

 Can you identify the missing numbers here?

1 100, ____, 98, ____, 96, ____, 94, ____.

2 57, ____, 55, ____, ____, ____, 51, 50.

3 83, ____, ____, 80, ____, ____, ____, 76.

4 41, ____, ____, 38, ____, 36, ____.

5 ____, 68, ____, 66, ____, 64, ____.

Let's count in fives. Read the number words aloud and draw the missing beads.

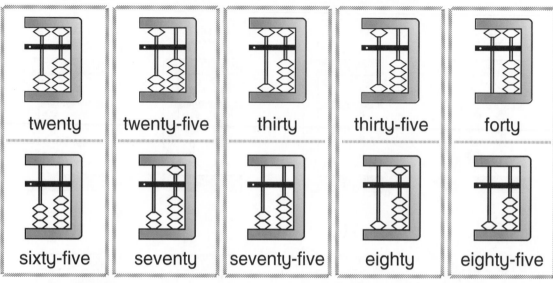

twenty | twenty-five | thirty | thirty-five | forty

sixty-five | seventy | seventy-five | eighty | eighty-five

Let's count in tens. Read the number words aloud and draw the missing beads.

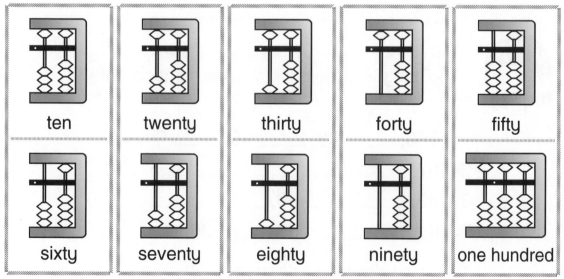

ten | twenty | thirty | forty | fifty

sixty | seventy | eighty | ninety | one hundred

Enrichment Activity A

Answer the questions below to solve this crossword puzzle.

		5		4		10					
								7			
		6				9					
	3										
	¹t	h	i	r	²t	e	e	n		12	
					w						
8					e		11				
13					n						
				¹⁴t							
				y							

Across →

1. $3 + 10 = \underline{13}$
3. $13 - 8 = \underline{\hphantom{00}}$
5. 5, ___, 15, 20.
7. $15 - 9 = \underline{\hphantom{00}}$
9. $12 - 11 = \underline{\hphantom{00}}$
11. 3, ___, 5, 6.
13. $6 + 5 = \underline{\hphantom{00}}$
14. 13, ___, 11, 10.

Down ↓

2. 10, __20__, 30, 40.
4. $\underline{\hphantom{00}} + 0 = 9$
6. $12 + 6 = \underline{\hphantom{00}}$
7. $4 + 3 = \underline{\hphantom{00}}$
8. $4 - 4 = \underline{\hphantom{00}}$
10. $7 - 5 = \underline{\hphantom{00}}$
12. $9 - 6 = \underline{\hphantom{00}}$

Enrichment Activity B

Fill in the blanks with **+** or **−** and solve the problems below.

1 Jenny has 3 cats. Devi has 8 cats. How many cats are there altogether?

$$8 \;(+)\; 3 = (11)$$

2 Andi has 6 fish. He gives 3 fish to Ah Wai. How many fish does Andi have left?

$$6 \;(\;)\; 3 = (\;)$$

3 There are 18 rambutans in the basket. Devi eats 7 rambutans from the basket. How many rambutans are left?

$$18 \;(\;)\; 7 = (\;)$$

4 On Zura's birthday, she receives 12 balloons. 5 balloons burst. How many balloons does she have now?

$$12 \;(\;)\; 5 = (\;)$$

5 Ah Wai has 14 toy cars. Andi has 4 toy cars more than Ah Wai. How many toy cars does Andi have?

$$14 \;(\;)\; 4 = (\;)$$

How many blue, yellow, red and green marbles should they colour? Answer the questions and help them colour the marbles correctly.

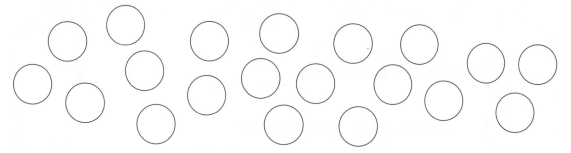

How many **blue** marbles should I colour?

What is seventeen minus twelve?

How many **yellow** marbles should I colour?

What is one more than six?

How many **red** marbles should I colour?

What is zero plus three?

How many **green** marbles should I colour?

What is eleven minus six?

Enrichment Activity D

Mark ✔ if it is correct or ✗ if it is wrong.

1. 5 and 6 are equal. ✗

2. 1 more than fifteen is 16.

3. 1 ten and 3 ones is thirteen.

4. The little friend of 2 is 8.

5. Nine is less than seven.

6. Eighteen minus nine equals eleven.

7. Eleven plus seven equals seventeen.

8. The big friend of 3 is 5.

9. 12 is less than 11.

10. Fourteen is 1 ten and 4 ones.

Enrichment Activity E

Can you guess my cat's name?

A	E	H	I	N	R	S
11	5	16	10	7	14	9

(1) 3 + 6 = (9) ➡ (S)

(2) 8 + 8 = ( ) ➡ ( )

(3) 12 – 7 = ( ) ➡ ( )

(4) 7 + 7 = ( ) ➡ ( )

(5) 15 – 5 = ( ) ➡ ( )

(6) 16 – 9 = ( ) ➡ ( )

(7) 5 + 6 = ( ) ➡ ( )

Match the answers to the alphabets to discover my cat's name. Write the alphabets below.

(1) (2) (3) (4) (5) (6) (7)

Jenny's cat's name is

| S | | | | | | |

Enrichment Activity F

Can you solve these mentally?

3 + 4 = ☐	☐ + 3 = 7	7 − 3 = ☐
8 + 1 = ☐	1 + ☐ = 9	9 − 1 = ☐
2 + 5 = ☐	☐ + 2 = 7	7 − 2 = ☐
3 + 3 = ☐	☐ + 3 = 6	6 − 3 = ☐
5 + 3 = ☐	☐ + 5 = 8	8 − 5 = ☐
1 + 2 = ☐	2 + ☐ = 3	3 − 2 = ☐
4 + 5 = ☐	☐ + 4 = 9	9 − 4 = ☐
0 + 6 = ☐	6 + ☐ = 6	6 − 6 = ☐
1 + 7 = ☐	7 + ☐ = 8	8 − 7 = ☐
2 + 3 = ☐	☐ + 2 = 5	5 − 2 = ☐

Solve these!

7 + 11 = ☐	18 − 11 = ☐
5 + 9 = ☐	14 − 9 = ☐
9 + 9 = ☐	18 − 9 = ☐
13 + 3 = ☐	16 − 13 = ☐
8 + 6 = ☐	14 − 6 = ☐